‘The bin men! The bin men!’ said Ken.

Ken had a job to do. 'I will run and get the bins and the box,' said Ken.
Ken got the big red box.

Ken got Mum's bin.
Ken got Dad's bin.
Ken got Ann's bin.

'Pop the bins on the mat and the tin cans in the box,' said Mum.

‘I will toss the tin cans in the box,’ said Ken.

Ken missed the box.

The tin cans fell on the mat.

‘No! No! It is a big mess,’ said Mum.
‘Put the tin cans in the box.’
‘I’ll fix it,’ said Ken.

Ken put all the tin cans in the box.
The bin men got the bins and the
boxes.

‘Yes. Ken did the bins well. A kiss for Ken,’
said Mum.

Homes Sweet Homes

Poems by James Carter

Illustrations by Dominique Mertens

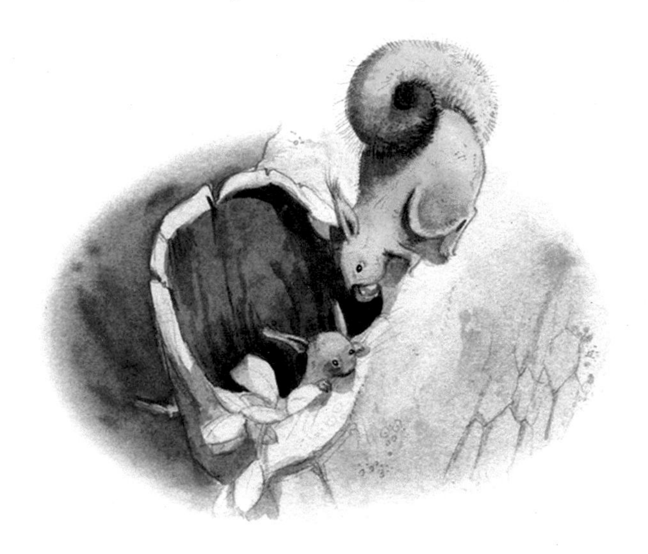

Collins

Contents

Home

A *web* or a *shell*
or a *hole* is a home
from deep in the *sea*
to up in a *tree*
home is *whatever*
you *want* it to be

A *cave* or an *egg*
or a *nest* is a home
the *busiest* place
or all on your *own*
wherever you *love*
the *best* is your home ...

your *home*
sweet
home!

Worm!

Little
worm,
how
do you
do?
I'd stay
put if
I was
you,
down
below
and out
of view.
Or
you'll
get
squished
beneath
my
shoe!

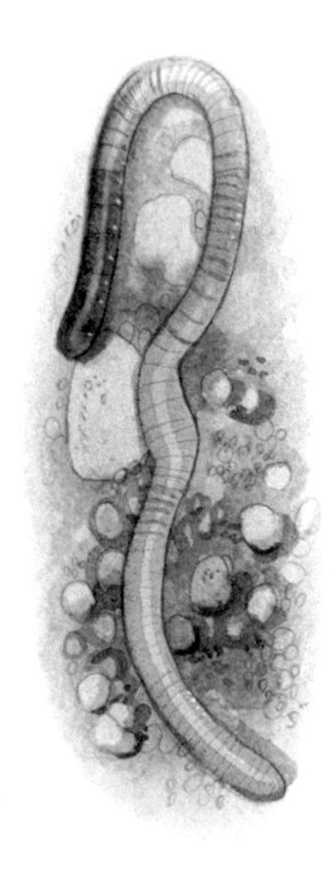

Dandelion

Dandelion!
You're no weed.
You're a clever
plant indeed!

First you wear
a yellow frock.
Then you turn
into a clock!

Wild Weed

Weed, weed,
you don't care,
for you will
settle anywhere.

Pavements, parks,
in grass or sand.
Wow, you really
get around!

Tree House

Meet the family
in this tree:
squirrel, robin,
moth make three.

Whose home is it,
this house so tall?
The three all share.
There's room for all!

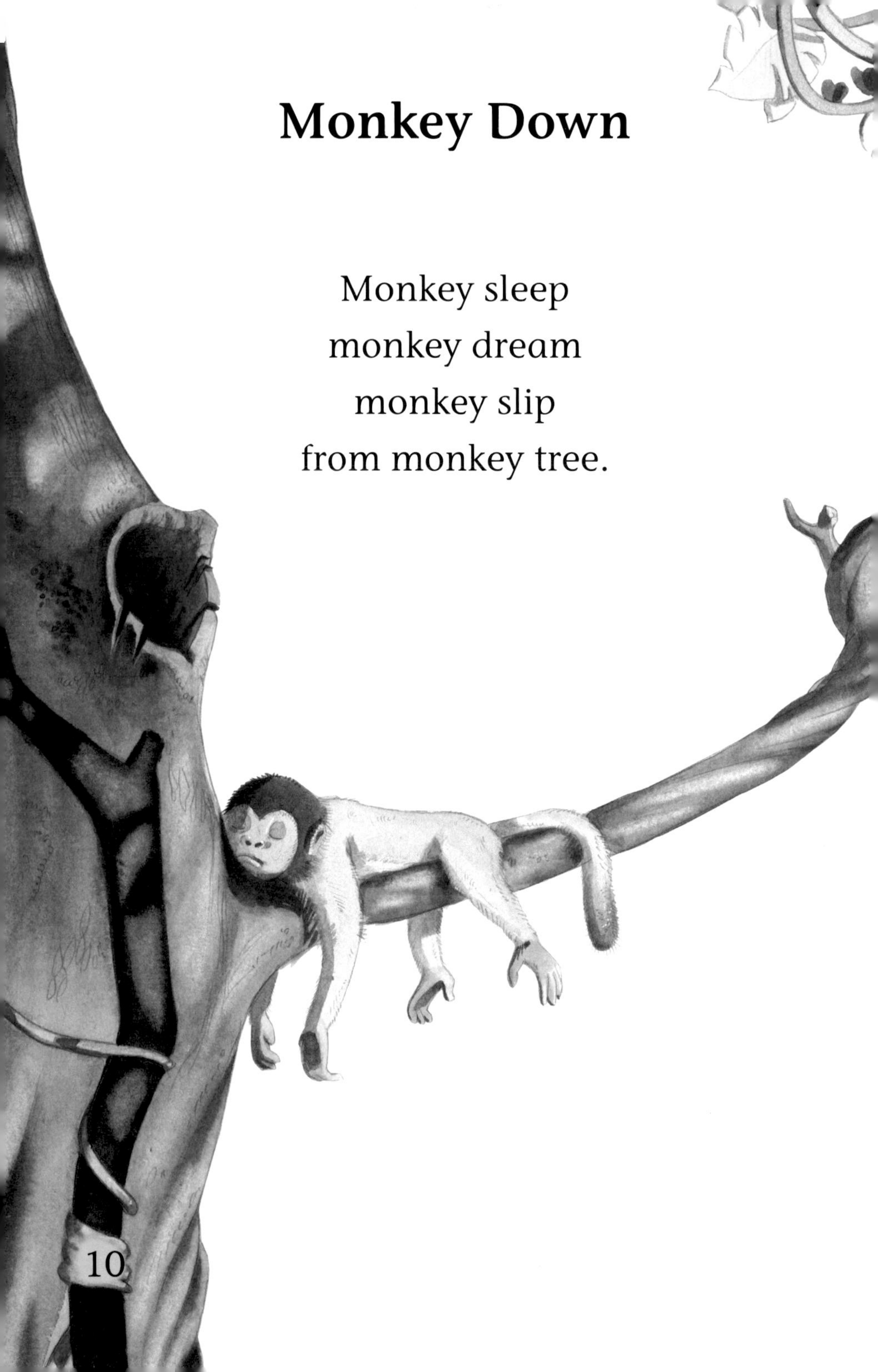

Monkey Down

Monkey sleep
monkey dream
monkey slip
from monkey tree.

Monkey fall
monkey down
monkey head
for monkey ground.

Monkey tail
monkey fast
monkey wrap
round monkey
branch.

Monkey swing
monkey sway
monkey snooze
all monkey day!

The Pond

Now it seems
like a dream
that June afternoon
when we found
the pond
by the path.

And the pond
was alive, brimful,
bristling, wriggling
with brand new life.

And you cupped
your hands,
skimmed through
the water,
as one little tickler
twitched in your palm;
just a blob for a body
and a pointy tail,
so black, like soot,
like a miniature whale:
such a restless soul
is a tadpole.

Millipede!

Millipede, millipede,
tell me do ...
how long does it take
to put on each shoe –

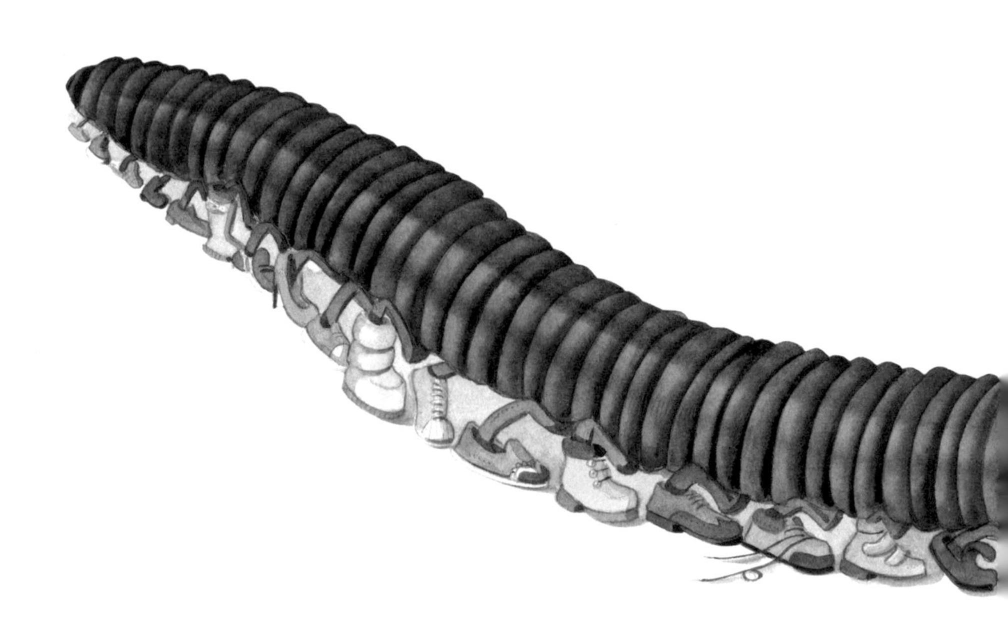

all thousand of them?
Oh, what a to-do!
I'm sorry to say,
I'm glad I'm not you!

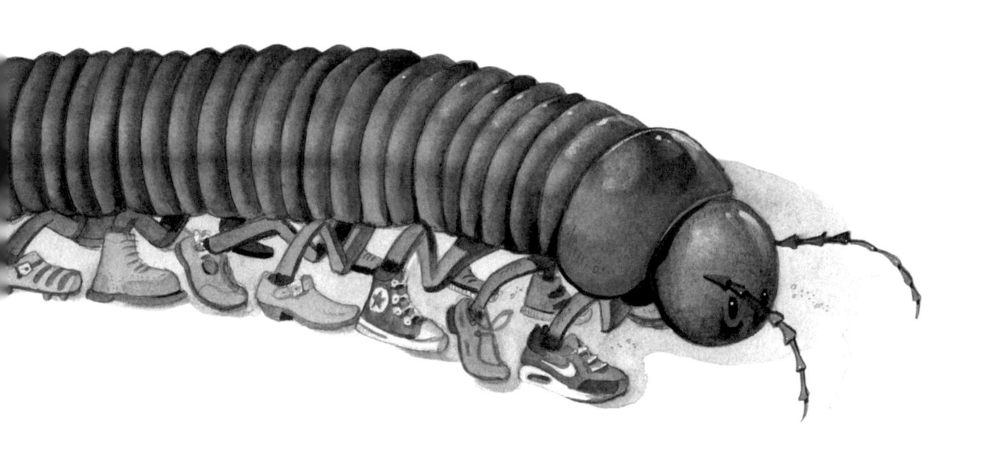

Spiky

I have two tiny,
shiny eyes.
And on my back?
A coat of spikes.

And with my snout
I sniff around
to find my supper
in the ground.

My sight you see
is clear as fog.
Me? I am a ...
hedgehog!

The Baobab (Bay-o-bab)

If ever
you're in Africa
do take
the time to see

the baobab
stood upside-down,
the topsy-turvy
tree!

***Sun*flower**

Sunflower, funflower
tall as the trees
crown like the sunshine
head full of seeds.

Here comes a cool breeze
swish and sway
sunflower, funflower
dance all day!

The Weather Tree

Said
the tree, come
hide under me. Whether
sun, whether rain – come
time and again. Whatever
the weather, I'll be
your umbrella!
!!!!
!!!!
!!!!
!!!!
!!!!
!!!!!
!!!!!!!

Homes sweet homes...

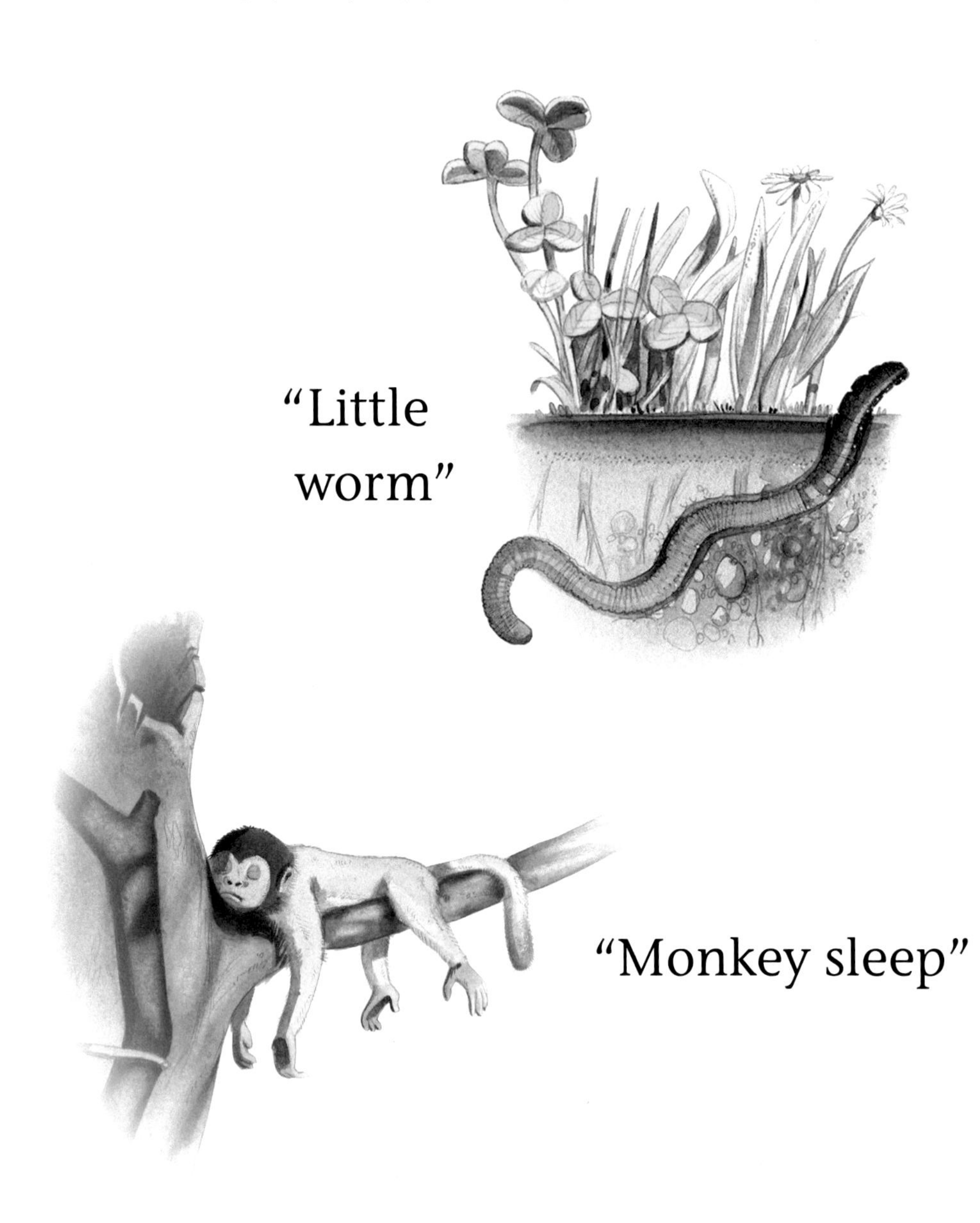

“Little
worm”

“Monkey sleep”

"such a restless
soul is a tadpole"

"Millipede, millipede,
tell me do"

"Me? I am a ...
hedgehog!"

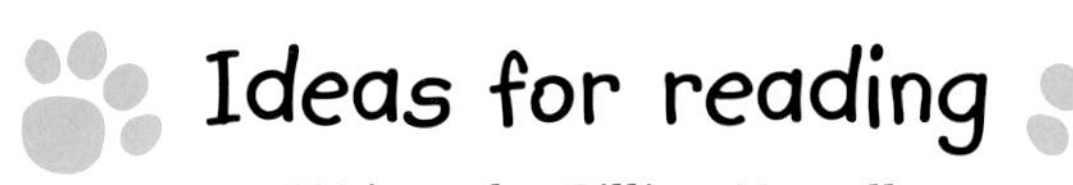

Ideas for reading

Written by Gillian Howell
Primary Literacy Consultant

Learning objectives: read words containing common suffixes; recognise simple recurring literary language in stories and poetry; discuss favourite words and phrases; participate in discussion about books, poems and other works that are read to them and those that they can read for themselves, taking turns and listening to what others say

Curriculum links: Science

Interest words: busiest, squished, dandelion, squirrel, bristling, wriggling, miniature, whale, thousand, spiky, baobab, weather

Word count: 427

Resources: modelling materials; pictures of animals and of animal homes.

Getting started

This book can be read over two or more reading sessions.

- Look at the cover illustration and read the title to the children.
- Discuss what makes a home with the children. Ask them what they like about their own homes.
- Ask them to speculate on what might be inside this book and give reasons for their opinions based on the cover illustration and title.
- Turn to the back cover and read the blurb. Ask them to describe any features of poems they think might be in the book.

Reading and responding

- Read pp2–5 to the children and ask them to read the rest of the poems.
- As they read, help the children identify different poetic features and forms, e.g. rhyme, rhythm, simile, shape poems etc.
- On p14, note the words with the *–ing ending: bristling, wriggling.* Help the children read the words, focussing on the common *–ing ending.*